CHESTER'S MUSIC PUZZLES

By Carol
With Illust
Wendy H
Chester's Piano Books

For Patsy Anderson — Enjoy the Puzzles!

INTRODUCTION

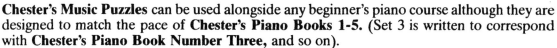

To the Teacher

Chester's Music Puzzles can be used alongside any beginner's piano course although they are designed to match the pace of **Chester's Piano Books 1-5.** (Set 3 is written to correspond with **Chester's Piano Book Number Three,** and so on).

They are for young beginners (5 years upwards) and can be used from the very first lesson. Each set is carefully graded to take into account the development of the pupils' reading and writing skills.

To start with, give your pupil the folder with just Paper 1 in it. The other papers can be handed out as the pupil progresses. Space has been left for stars — it is well worth keeping a supply to reward your pupils! There is also a certificate to be won when each set has been completed!

The information boxes are as simple as possible, to teach or remind the pupil. They are also invaluable for parents helping their children.

It is important that written work should be taught hand-in-hand with practical playing, to make the *"language"* of music much easier and more natural to learn.

To the Parent

These papers aim to give young children a real sense of enjoyment as they begin to learn the language of music. As you and your children go through each paper with Chester the Frog and his friends, learning to read and write music becomes as natural as learning to read and write words. Read through each information box with your child before trying the questions!

To the Pupil

Make sure that you use a B or a 2B pencil. Try to get a star every time! Enjoy yourselves!

Carol Barratt ♫ ♪

CHESTER'S SET MUSIC PUZZLES

CONTENTS

Topics

Consolidates material from Sets 1 & 2, plus Adding Rhythms to Words, Tones, Semitones, Accidentals, Slurs, Intervals, Lines and Spaces (rhymes to remember them), Octave signs, Major Scales **(C,F,G)** Leger Lines.

New Notes

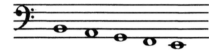 

New Note and Rest Values

Dotted notes and rests

New Time Signatures

C $\frac{3}{2}$ $\frac{3}{8}$ $\frac{2}{2}$ $\frac{4}{2}$ $\frac{6}{8}$

New Signs and Words

ff *pp* *mf* *mp* tenuto

CHESTER'S MUSIC PUZZLES SET 2

Name ....

FIND THE NOTES

1. Some of the notes on the keyboard have been numbered.
   Write these notes on the staves below.

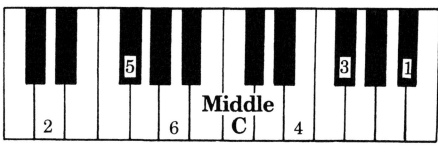

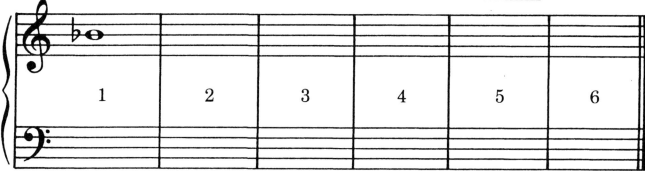

RHYTHMS AND BEATS

2. Circle the notes that you don't actually play.

   Then write down the number of beats in the Time Signature.

3. Add the missing dots to fill each Bar.   Then finish writing the counts.

(3   4)   1 - 2 - 3   4 +

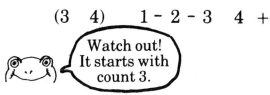

Watch out!
It starts with
count 3.

ADDING RHYTHMS TO WORDS

4. Clap out a rhythm as you say these words.

"Apples | peanuts   celery and   eggs."
      >   >   >   >

Now draw a Bar-Line in front of each > above, so that the >s come on the first beat of the Bar. The first one has been done for you!

The first beat is the STRONGEST!

Your rhythm probably sounds like this:

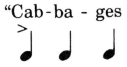

5. Write a rhythm for these words. Try saying it and clapping it first.

"Cab-ba - ges   peas   and   beans   and   leeks."

The words in brackets are Italian

MORE SIGNS

p (piano) → Soft	***f*** (forte) → Loud
pp (pianissimo) → Very Soft	***ff*** (fortissimo) → Very Loud

6. Would you use ***ff*** or ***pp*** for a Lullaby?

CHESTER'S MUSIC PUZZLES SET 2

PAPER 2

Name ....

TONES AND SEMITONES

Semitone → One key to the very next key (black or white).
Tone → One key to the next key, but with one key (black or white) in between.

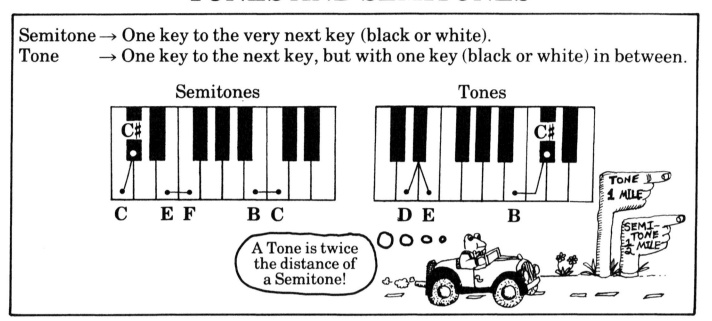

1. Write **S** for Semitone or **T** for Tone.
   Use the picture of the Keyboard to help you.

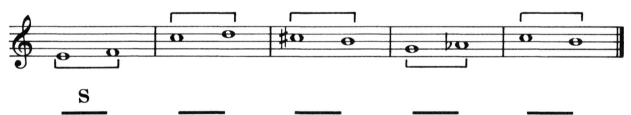

S ___ ___ ___ ___ ___

2. Write Tones above each note.

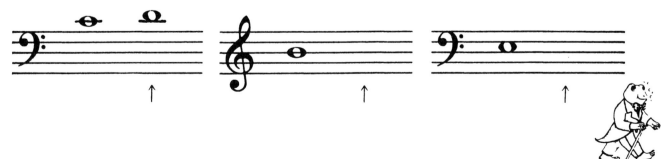

3. Write Semitones above each note.

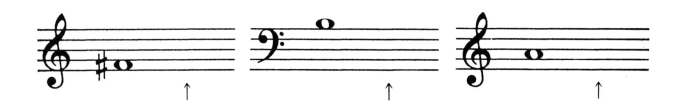

OCTAVES

4. Name the notes.   Then write them an octave lower in the 𝄢:

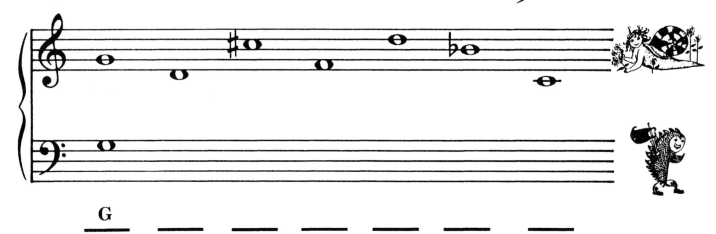

G _ _ _ _ _ _ _ _ _

NOTE VALUES

5. Pretend this block is a 𝅝

𝅝

Write notes of the correct value in each of the blocks below.

6. One note is missing from each Bar.   Write in the missing notes.

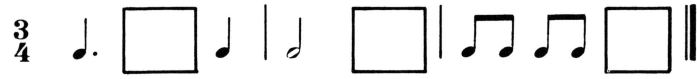

CHESTER'S MUSIC PUZZLES

Name ....

TEN MORE NOTES

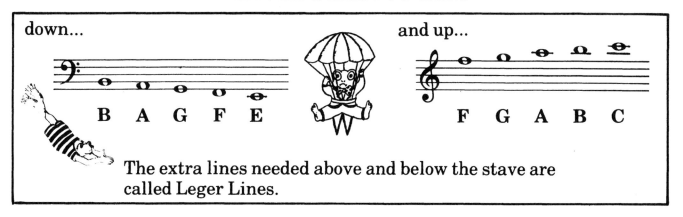

The extra lines needed above and below the stave are called Leger Lines.

NOTE READING

1. Write the name of each note in its box.

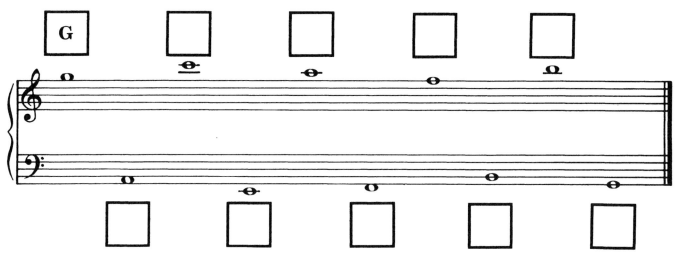

NOTE WRITING

2. Using the new notes, write ♩s for each letter-name given.

Look at the stems

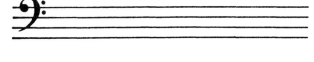

A   E   G

B   A   C

RESTING!

3. Add the missing Rests.

ACCIDENTALS

An Accidental is either a ♭ , ♮ or ♯ .

4. Make the second note a Semitone higher by drawing an Accidental before it. Then name the notes.

F   F♯

RHYTHM

5. Chester has forgotten his rhythm.   Can you help him remember it?

"Ches-ter   the   Frog"

3/4

6. Write your name and add a rhythm.

Name:

Rhythm:

CHESTER'S MUSIC PUZZLES

SET

Name ....

MUSIC DICTIONARY

mf (mezzo forte) → Moderately Loud.

mp (mezzo piano) → Moderately Soft.

(tenuto) → Stress the note.

→ Common Time ($\frac{4}{4}$)

1. Draw the signs in the boxes.

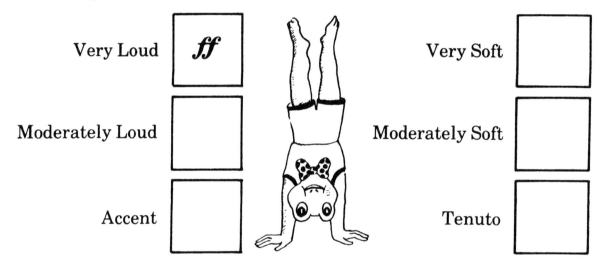

Very Loud   *ff*   Very Soft

Moderately Loud   Moderately Soft

Accent   Tenuto

MISSING NOTES

2. One note is missing from each Bar.   Write in the missing notes.

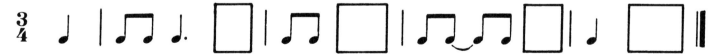

3. Write Tones above these notes.   Look at Set 3, Paper 2 to remind you.

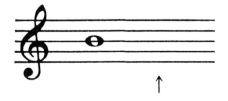

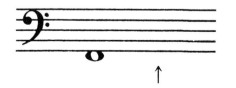

MORE ABOUT TIME SIGNATURES

The beat is not always a ♩

The bottom number in the Time Signature shows the *type* of beat.

Number of beats

Type of beat

This is worked out from the 𝅝

bottom numbers
$\begin{cases} 2 = \text{♩ beats (𝅝 = 2 Minims)} \\ 4 = \text{♩ beats (𝅝 = 4 Crotchets)} \\ 8 = \text{♪ beats (𝅝 = 8 Quavers)} \end{cases}$

Examples:

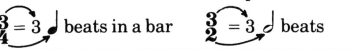

$\frac{3}{4}$ = 3 ♩ beats in a bar $\frac{3}{2}$ = 3 ♩ beats $\frac{3}{8}$ = 3 ♪ beats

---

4. Add the bottom numbers to make correct Time Signatures.

↑ 1 2 3 4   ↑ 1 2 3 4   ↑ 1 2   ↑ 1 2 3

THINGS TO ADD

5. Add a Bass Clef.
    Add the Time Signature for Common Time.
    Play it through and write some notes in Bar 4.
    Add Phrase-Marks.
    Look for Semitones and mark them with ⌐⌐.

CHESTER'S MUSIC PUZZLES

Name ....

SLURS

A Slur is a curved line covering two or more notes, like an umbrella. These notes are to be played smoothly (legato).

2-note slur   3-note slur

1. Slur the Crotchets in sets of 2s.

2. Tick the tied notes and put **Sl.** by each Slur.

Sl.

SPOT THE MISTAKES

3. Cross out the wrong letter-names.

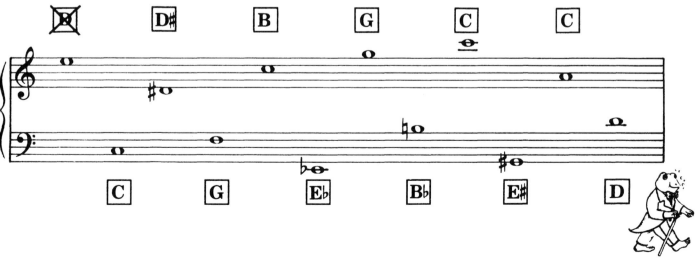

INTERVALS

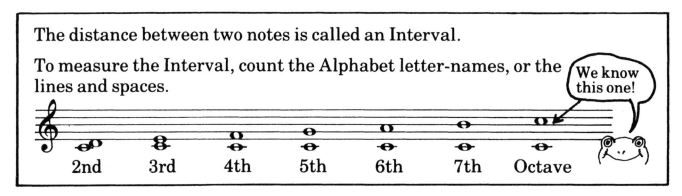

The distance between two notes is called an Interval.

To measure the Interval, count the Alphabet letter-names, or the lines and spaces.

We know this one!

2nd   3rd   4th   5th   6th   7th   Octave

4. Tick the correct box.

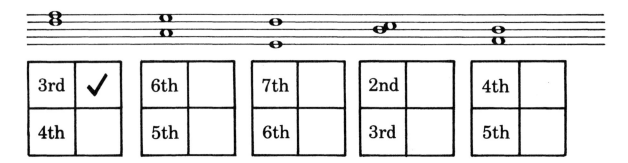

3rd	✓
4th	

6th	
5th	

7th	
6th	

2nd	
3rd	

4th	
5th	

5. Copy these Intervals.   Then name them.

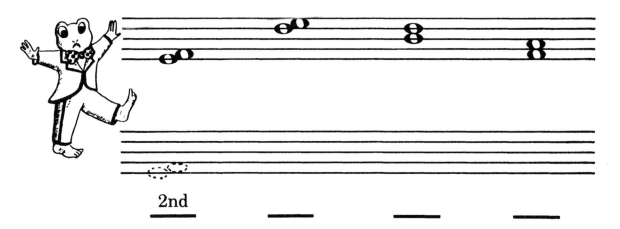

2nd   ___   ___   ___   ___

6. Write 2nds and 3rds, as Crotchets. (One after the other).

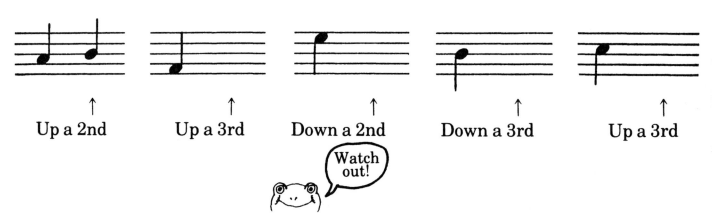

Up a 2nd   Up a 3rd   Down a 2nd   Down a 3rd   Up a 3rd

Watch out!

CHESTER'S MUSIC PUZZLES

SET

Name ....

CHANGE AROUND

1. Add the Time Signature.   Then re-write this tune putting Rests in place of notes, and notes (on any line or space) in place of Rests.

LINES AND SPACES

Words to help you remember:

LINES

E   G   B   D   F

Eight Great Big   Dancing Frogs

SPACES

F   A   C   E

**Frogs Always Croak Easily
(also spells FACE)**

2.

What note lives on the third line?

What note lives in the first space?

What note lives on the fifth line?

What note lives in the fourth space?

What note lives on the second line?

croak!

$\frac{6}{8}$ A NEW KIND OF TIME SIGNATURE

> There are two main ♩. beats in each Bar and each beat is divided into 3 ♪ s

> Think of $\frac{6}{8}$ as $\frac{2}{♩.}$ $\frac{6}{8}$

> Count 6 at first to make it easy. Put an accent on the first count and a stress on the fourth.
>
>
>
> Count: 1 2 3 4 5 6   1-2 3 4-5-6
> Then: 1   2   1   2
>
> ♪ = ♩. Rest

3. Add the missing stems and beams to the notes below to make each Bar add up to the Time Signature.

This is the beam.

TIME SIGNATURES

4. Add the correct Time Signature to each Bar.

TONES AND SEMITONES

5. Write **T** for Tone or **S** for Semitone by the brackets.

CHESTER'S MUSIC PUZZLES

SET 7

PAPER 7

Name ....

OCTAVE SIGNS

8ve ┄┄┄┄┄┄┄┐   → This sign tells you to play the note or notes an Octave *higher* than written.

8ve ┄┄┄┄┄┄┘   → This sign tells you to play the note or notes an Octave *lower* than written.

1. Write out these Bars again without using the Octave signs.

LINES AND SPACES

Words to help you remember: 𝄢

LINES						SPACES			
G	B	D	F	A		A	C	E	G

Great Big Dancing Frogs Again   Active Chester Enjoys Games

2.

What note lives on the fourth line? ☐   What note lives in the first space? ☐

What note lives in the second space? ☐   What note lives on the third line? ☐

What note lives on the second line? ☐

TIME SIGNATURES

3. Work out the Time Signatures for the Bars below.
   Then write some notes to fill each Bar.

2 ♩ beats

4 ♩ beats

2 ♩. beats

3 ♩ beats

NOTE WRITING

4. Using the notes ♩ and ♩ ,

   write the notes as ♩. for each letter-name given.

| G | A | E | F |

| G | B | C | E | A |

COPYCAT

5. Copy these three Bars.
   Then find the Semitones and mark them with ⌐ .

Don't forget to look at the Key Signature

CHESTER'S MUSIC PUZZLES

SET 2

PAPER 8

Name ....

MAJOR SCALES

A Scale is a "musical ladder" made up of Tones and Semitones.
It has 8 notes in alphabetical order.

The first note of the Scale is called the key-note

1 2 3 4 5 6 7 8

C D E F G A B C

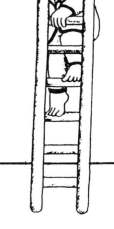

1. Number the notes.
   Then mark **S** for Semitone or **T** for Tone under the brackets.

C MAJOR SCALE

T

2. Now try the same in the Bass Clef.

Every Major Scale has this pattern →Semitones between 3–4 and 7–8

OTHER MAJOR SCALES

> ♯s and ♭s are needed in the other Major Scales,
> to keep to the Major Scale pattern.

3. Add ⌐ to the Semitones, and mark them **S**.

F Major

1   2   3   4   5   6   7   8

G Major

1   2   3   4   5   6   7   8

ADDING RHYTHMS TO WORDS

4. Write rhythms for these words.

"Ches - ter   is   the   great - est!"

$\frac{2}{4}$

"Bread   and   jam   and   slic - es   of   ham."

$\frac{3}{8}$
Watch out!

RESTS AND NOTES

5. Draw notes which have these Rests.

LOOK! Rests can be dotted too!

CHESTER'S MUSIC PUZZLES

Name ....

KEY SIGNATURES

The notes in a piece are usually taken from a scale.
The ♯s and ♭s of this scale are shown in the Key Signature.
Here are the Key Signatures for two scales.

↓ F Major   and   ↓ G Major

Look at Set 3, Paper 7, Question 5. This piece is in the Key of **G** major.

1. Write out the scale of **G** Major 𝄞 without using a Key Signature.
   Add ⌐ to the Semitones, and mark them **S**. Check they make the major Scale
   pattern.

1   2   3   4   5   6   7   8

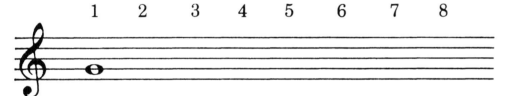

2. From the Scale that you have written, work out the Key Signature.

3. Write out the Scale of **F** Major 𝄢 without using a Key Signature.
   Add ⌐ to the Semitones, and mark them **S**.

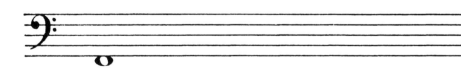

4. From the Scale you have written, work out the Key Signature.

5. Look at the Bars below. Then write the key of each one in the box.

Key of ☐ Major   Key of ☐ Major

SIX MORE NOTES

6. Copy these notes.

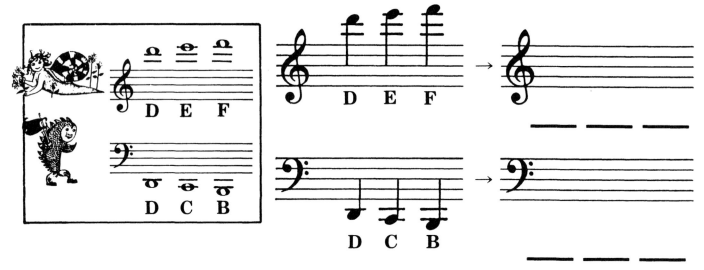

SLUR OR STACCATO?

7. Add 2-note Slurs or Staccato dots to the notes below.
   The words will tell you where to put them.

Hop,   hop,   slid - ing, smooth - ly   glid - ing,   bounce,   bounce.

8. The piece above is in the key of ☐ Major.

CHESTER'S MUSIC PUZZLES

Name ....

OLD NOTES ON NEW LEGER LINES

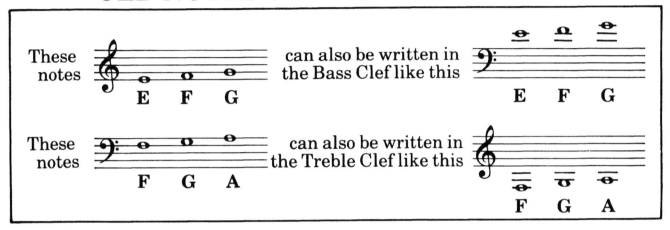

These notes 𝄞 E F G — can also be written in the Bass Clef like this 𝄢 E F G

These notes 𝄢 F G A — can also be written in the Treble Clef like this 𝄞 F G A

1. Write the new Leger Line notes as Minims.

G E F

A F G

2. Write the five keys on the keyboard below in two ways.

(i) in the 𝄢 (ii) in the 𝄞 Both answers use some Leger Lines.

Middle
A B C D E

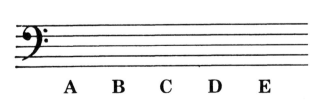

A B C D E

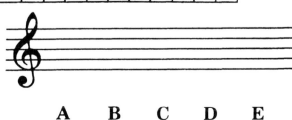

A B C D E

INTERVALS

3. Write 4ths and 5ths, as Crotchets.

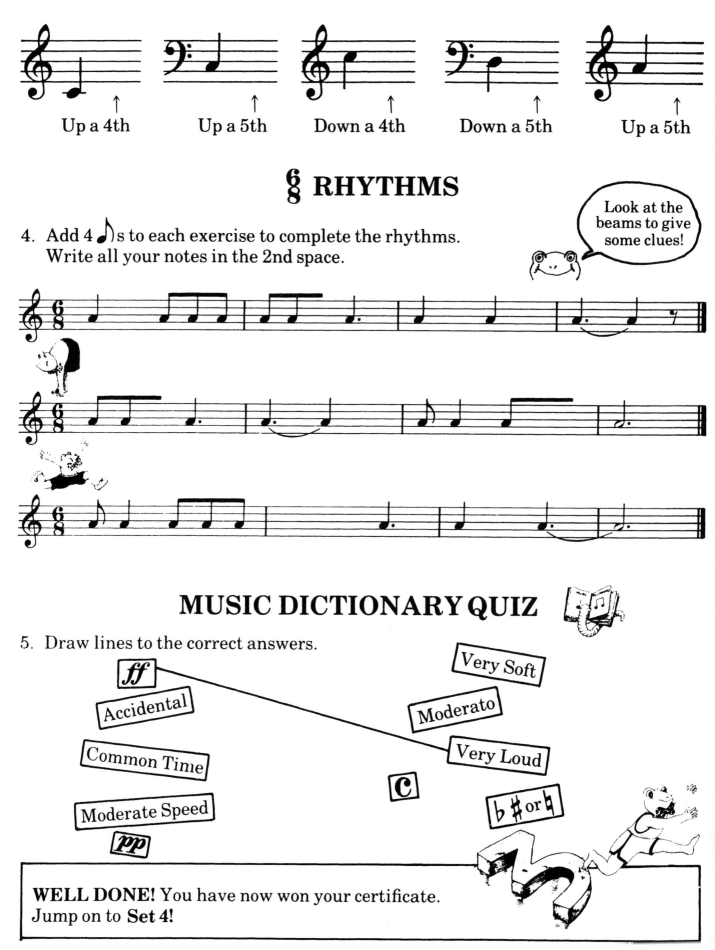

Up a 4th   Up a 5th   Down a 4th   Down a 5th   Up a 5th

⁶⁄₈ RHYTHMS

4. Add 4 ♪s to each exercise to complete the rhythms.
   Write all your notes in the 2nd space.

Look at the beams to give some clues!

MUSIC DICTIONARY QUIZ

5. Draw lines to the correct answers.

ff   Very Soft

Accidental   Moderato

Common Time   Very Loud

        C

Moderate Speed   ♭ ♯ or ♮

pp

WELL DONE! You have now won your certificate.
Jump on to **Set 4!**

CHESTER'S CERTIFICATE

This award certifies that

_____

has successfully completed
Chester's Music Puzzles Set 3
and is ready to leap ahead
to **Set 4.**

Well Done!

_____ Teacher

_____ Date

Carol Barratt